Balance
Math™ & More!

Level 3

SERIES TITLES
Balance Math™ & More!
Level 1 ▪ Level 2 ▪ Level 3

Written by
Robert Femiano

Graphic Design by
Scott Slyter

Cover Design by
Annette Langenstein

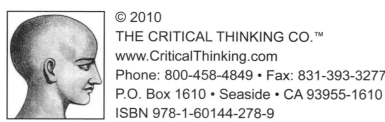

© 2010
THE CRITICAL THINKING CO.™
www.CriticalThinking.com
Phone: 800-458-4849 • Fax: 831-393-3277
P.O. Box 1610 • Seaside • CA 93955-1610
ISBN 978-1-60144-278-9

Mixed Sources
Product group from well-managed
forests and other controlled sources
www.fsc.org Cert no. SW-COC-002283
© 1996 Forest Stewardship Council

TABLE OF CONTENTS

The Value of *Balance Math* and More!

These activities sharpen students' critical thinking skills, computational skills, and develop algebraic reasoning. The first book in the series (Level 1) focuses on addition and subtraction of whole numbers. The second book (Level 2) focuses on multiplication and division of whole numbers, but has a few problems involving fractions. The third book (Level 3) involves addition, subtraction, division, and multiplication, as well as fractions and decimals. The spiraling difficulty level within each book is designed to scaffold a students' conceptual understanding of the targeted operations from beginning to advanced. Try one of these intriguing puzzles—and then try to stop!

Teaching Suggestions

Balance Math™ and More! activities are unique because their solution requires mathematical reasoning, critical thinking, and computational skills. This makes these problems fun, but challenging. I recommend teachers review the directions with students on all three types of puzzles (Inside-Out Math, Tic Tac Math, and Balance Math™) and jointly work through some of each, until students can demonstrate how to correctly solve them independently. After that, should students become stumped, I first encourage perseverance or 'think time' by reminding them that people do puzzles because they enjoy being puzzled. I also praise the effort and determination of students even more than the correct answer. But like all puzzlers, they may occasionally need a hint. For Inside-Out Math or Tic Tac Math puzzles, use the answer pages to provide them with the correct number needed next. You can jumpstart their thinking for Balance Math™ puzzles by using the hints provided on page 38.

Balance Math™: Students should examine the balanced scales to deduce and calculate the value of any one shape which can then be substituted on another balance and so on, until the solution is found. These puzzles are great stepping-stones to showing students the basics of balancing and solving algebraic equations.

Inside-Out Math: Students need to reverse their thinking, using the inverse relationships between addition and subtraction and multiplication with division to solve the puzzles.

Tic Tac Math: Three, four or five in a row wins, but can you figure out the correct order to complete all rows, columns, and diagonals?

About the Author

A longtime puzzle fan, Robert Femiano is a Seattle public school elementary educator and has been for most of his 35-year teaching career. For more than a decade of this time, he was also adjunct faculty at Seattle Pacific University, conducting math methods courses. His publications include *Algebraic Problem Solving in the Primary Grades* in the National Council for Teachers of Mathematics peer-reviewed journal and *Balance Benders*™ by The Critical Thinking Co.™. In 2002, he won the highest honor in education, the Presidential Award for Excellence in Mathematics and Science Teaching.

Use the balanced scales to find the missing numbers.

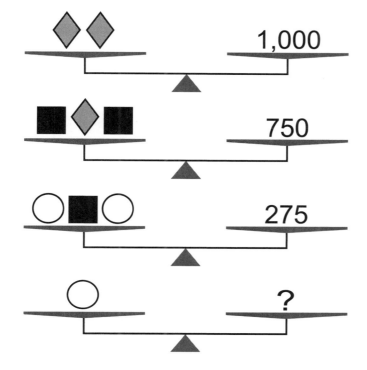

Problem 1

? = ...

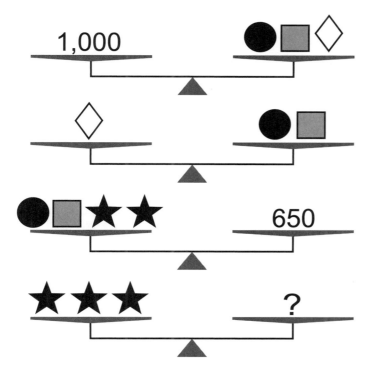

Problem 2

? = ...

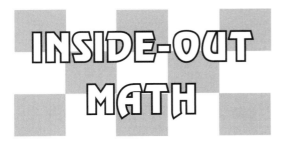

Use the clues to find the missing values.

Problem 1

a	a+c	a+d
100	**1,000**	**10,000**
b	b+c	b+d
	1,100	

c	d

Problem 2

a	a+c	a+d
	641	
b	b+c	b+d
174	**470**	**532**

c	d

Problem 3

a	a+c	a+d
		7,660
b	b+c	b+d
	8,012	**8,821**

c	d
4,288	

Problem 4

a	a+c	a+d
	22,214	**24,332**
b	b+c	b+d
		26,141

c	d
	13,487

Problem 5

a	a+c	a+d
	$2\frac{1}{4}$	
b	b+c	b+d
$2\frac{2}{3}$	$3\frac{1}{6}$	**4**

c	d

Problem 6

a	a+c	a+d
$\frac{1}{4}$	$\frac{7}{12}$	
b	b+c	b+d
	$\frac{5}{6}$	$1\frac{1}{6}$

c	d

Use the balanced scales to find the missing numbers.

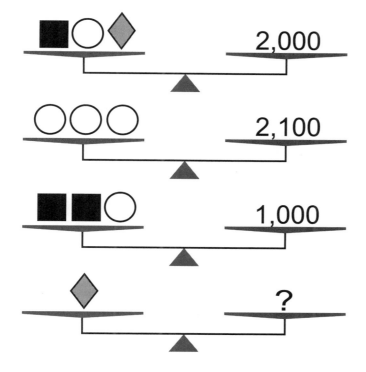

2,000

2,100

1,000

?

Problem 1

? = ...

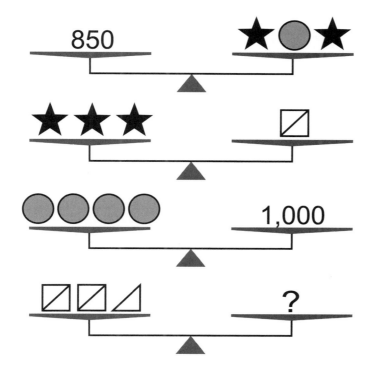

850

? =

Problem 2

? = ...

1,000

?

Use the balanced scales to find the missing numbers.

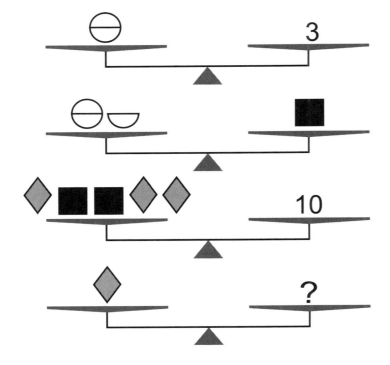

Problem 1

? = ...

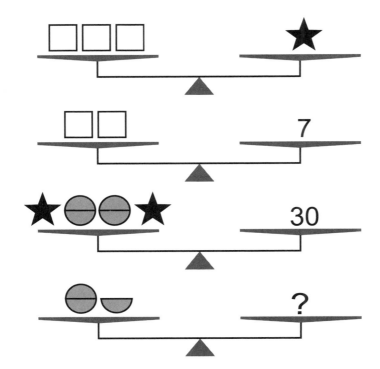

Problem 2

? = ...

Use the balanced scales to find the missing numbers.

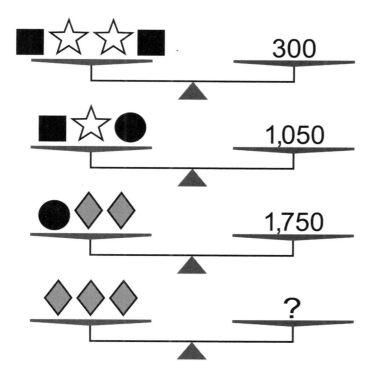

300

1,050

1,750

?

Problem 1

? = ...

13

10½

?

Problem 2

? = ...

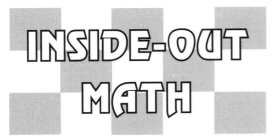

Use the clues to find the missing values.

Problem 1

a	a-c	a-d
10,000	....	8,990

b	b-c	b-d
....	28,889	28,990

c	d
....	....

Problem 2

a	a-c	a-d
....	245	....

b	b-c	b-d
804	326	448

c	d
....	....

Problem 3

a	a-c	a-d
....	3,675	344

b	b-c	b-d
....	....	2,407

c	d
2,367	....

Problem 4

a	a-c	a-d
....	7,728	1,649

b	b-c	b-d
....	10,761	....

c	d
....	11,358

Problem 5

a	a-c	a-d
$\frac{1}{2}$	$\frac{1}{4}$	....

b	b-c	b-d
....	$\frac{1}{2}$	$\frac{5}{8}$

c	d
....	....

Problem 6

a	a-c	a-d
....	$\frac{1}{4}$	$1\frac{1}{12}$

b	b-c	b-d
....	....	$1\frac{1}{4}$

c	d
$2\frac{1}{12}$	....

Use the balanced scales
to find the missing numbers.

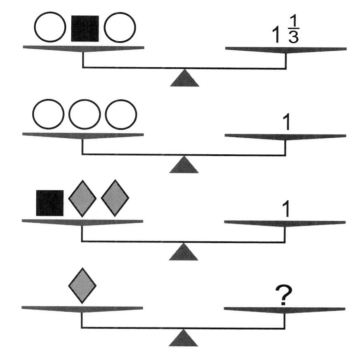

Problem 1

? = ...

Problem 2

? = ...

All rows, columns, and three numeral diagonals must add up to the same sum. Write the total and then fill in the empty spaces.

Problem 1

	730	
1,090	70	1,030

Total: _____

Problem 2

	104	120
	136	
152		

Total: _____

Problem 3

119		
	413	
	203	707

Total: _____

Problem 4

	27.2	19.2
	18.4	
	9.6	

Total: _____

Problem 5

		0.94
	1.27	
1.6	0.83	

Total: _____

Problem 6

0.619	1.039	1.459
		0.409

Total: _____

Use the balanced scales
to find the missing numbers.

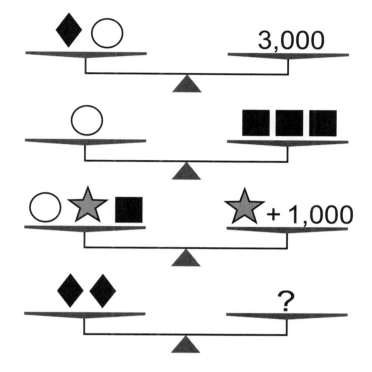

Problem 1

? = ...

Problem 2

? = ...

Use the balanced scales
to find the missing numbers.

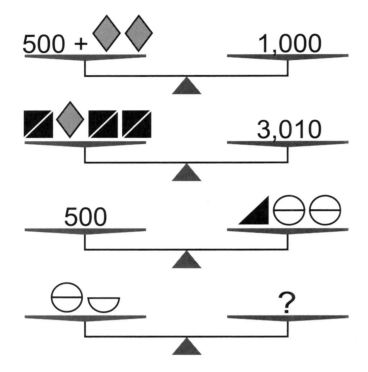

Problem 1

? = ...

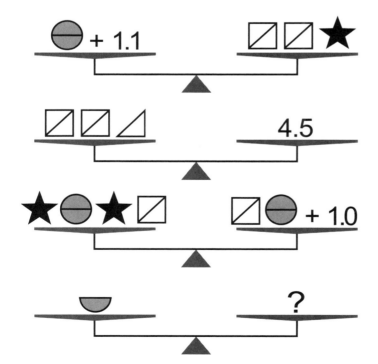

Problem 2

? = ...

INSIDE-OUT MATH

Use the clues to find the missing values.

Problem 1

a		a+c	a+d
$\frac{2}{3}$		$1\frac{5}{12}$	....
b		b+c	b+d
....		$1\frac{1}{6}$	$\frac{7}{12}$

c	d
....	....

Problem 2

a		a+c	a+d
....		....	$4\frac{1}{2}$
b		b+c	b+d
$1\frac{9}{10}$		$3\frac{1}{2}$	$2\frac{3}{5}$

c	d
....	....

Problem 3

a		a+c	a+d
....		$\frac{7}{12}$	$1\frac{1}{8}$
b		b+c	b+d
....		....	$1\frac{7}{12}$

c	d
$\frac{3}{8}$	....

Problem 4

a		a-c	a-d
....		....	$2\frac{1}{2}$
b		b-c	b-d
....		$2\frac{1}{3}$	$3\frac{1}{4}$

c	d
....	$\frac{5}{6}$

Problem 5

a		a-c	a-d
$6\frac{1}{7}$		$\frac{9}{14}$	$4\frac{25}{28}$
b		b-c	b-d
....		$2\frac{11}{18}$	....

c	d
....	....

Problem 6

a		a-c	a-d
$3\frac{2}{5}$		$1\frac{21}{40}$	....
b		b-c	b-d
....		$2\frac{43}{88}$	$1\frac{51}{110}$

c	d
....	....

Use the balanced scales
to find the missing numbers.

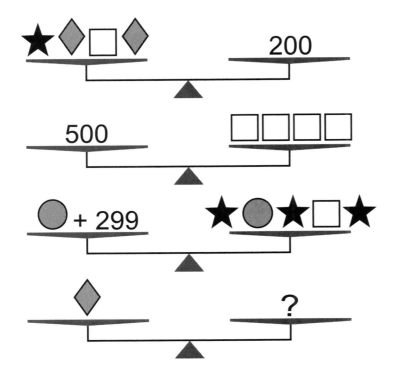

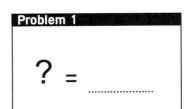

Problem 1

? = ...

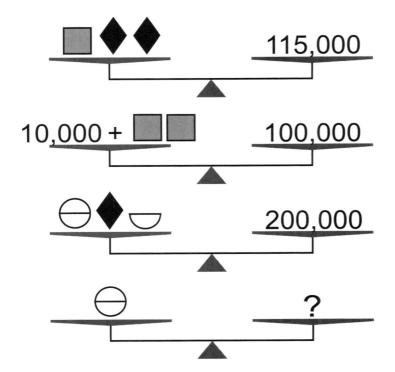

Problem 2

? = ...

All rows, columns, and three numeral diagonals must add up to the same sum. Write the total and then fill in the empty spaces.

Problem 1

	1	
	$1\frac{1}{4}$	
$\frac{1}{2}$	$1\frac{1}{2}$	

Total: _____

Problem 2

	$\frac{9}{16}$	$\frac{5}{8}$
	$\frac{3}{4}$	
$\frac{7}{8}$		

Total: _____

Problem 3

$\frac{2}{5}$		$\frac{3}{10}$
	$\frac{1}{4}$	
		$\frac{1}{10}$

Total: _____

Problem 4

		$\frac{1}{6}$
	$\frac{1}{8}$	
$\frac{1}{12}$		$\frac{1}{16}$

Total: _____

Problem 5

$\frac{1}{6}$		$\frac{1}{18}$
	$\frac{1}{12}$	
$\frac{1}{9}$		

Total: _____

Problem 6

		$-\frac{3}{400}$
		$\frac{1}{100}$
	$-\frac{1}{200}$	$-\frac{1}{400}$

Total: _____

Use the balanced scales
to find the missing numbers.

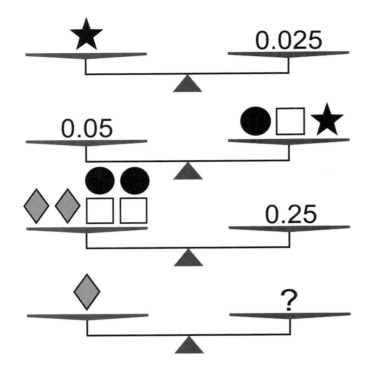

Problem 1

? = ...

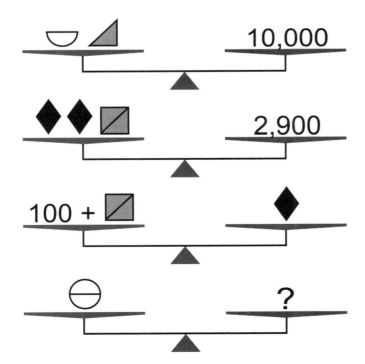

Problem 2

? = ...

Use the balanced scales
to find the missing numbers.

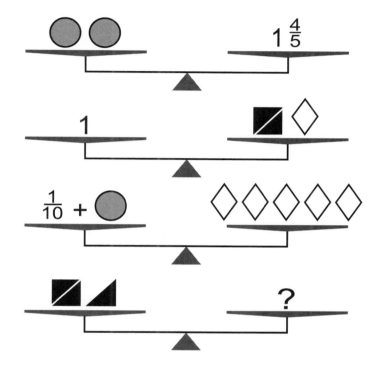

Problem 1

? = ...

Problem 2

? = ...

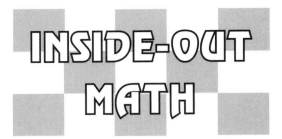

INSIDE-OUT MATH

Use the clues to find the missing values.

Problem 1

a	a+c	a+d
1.1	1.2	2.21

b	b+c	b+d
…………	0.11	…………

c	d
…………	…………

Problem 2

a	a+c	a+d
…………	…………	6.1

b	b+c	b+d
2.8	12.1	5.2

c	d
…………	…………

Problem 3

a	a+c	a+d
…………	0.055	0.01

b	b+c	b+d
…………	0.55	…………

c	d
0.05	…………

Problem 4

a	a−c	a−d
…………	2.7	0.027

b	b−c	b−d
…………	2.97	…………

c	d
…………	3.003

Problem 5

a	a−c	a−d
0.6	0.54	0.594

b	b−c	b−d
…………	…………	0.654

c	d
…………	…………

Problem 6

a	a−c	a−d
…………	0.901	…………

b	b−c	b−d
…………	0.91	1.0099

c	d
…………	0.0001

Use the balanced scales
to find the missing numbers.

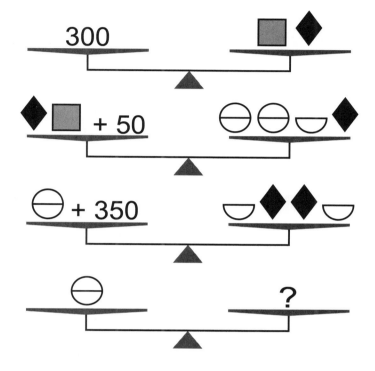

Problem 1

? = ...

Problem 2

? = ...

Use the balanced scales
to find the missing numbers.

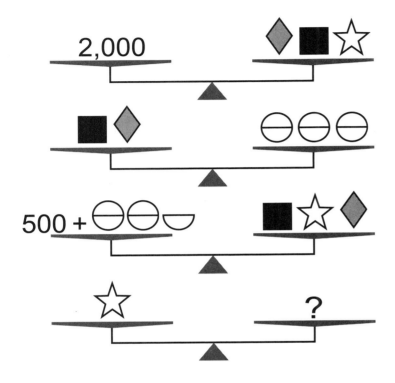

Problem 1

? = ...

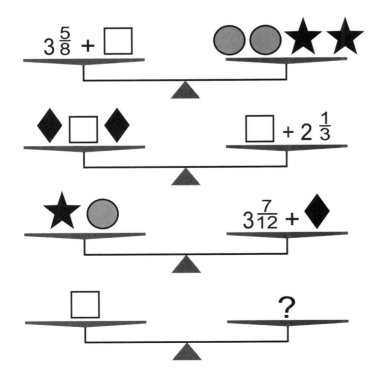

Problem 2

? = ...

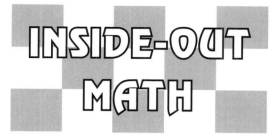

Use the clues to find the missing values.

Problem 1

a	a+c	a+d
$\dfrac{3}{4}$	$1\dfrac{7}{12}$	....
b	**b-c**	**b-d**
....	$\dfrac{2}{3}$	$\dfrac{5}{24}$

c	d
....	....

Problem 2

a	a-c	a-d
....	....	$\dfrac{11}{24}$
b	**b+c**	**b+d**
$\dfrac{3}{4}$	$\dfrac{19}{20}$	$1\dfrac{1}{8}$

c	d
....	....

Problem 3

a	a+c	a-d
....	$2\dfrac{17}{24}$	$1\dfrac{5}{24}$
b	**b-c**	**b+d**
....	....	$2\dfrac{5}{24}$

c	d
$\dfrac{5}{8}$	....

Problem 4

a	a+c	a+d
....	0.14	0.077
b	**b-c**	**b-d**
....	0.63	....

c	d
....	0.007

Problem 5

a	a-c	a-d
1.1	0.09	1.089
b	**b+c**	**b+d**
....	....	0.112

c	d
....	....

Problem 6

a	a+c	a-d
....	0.108	....
b	**b+c**	**b-d**
....	0.1899	0.09

c	d
0.099	....

Use the balanced scales
to find the missing numbers.

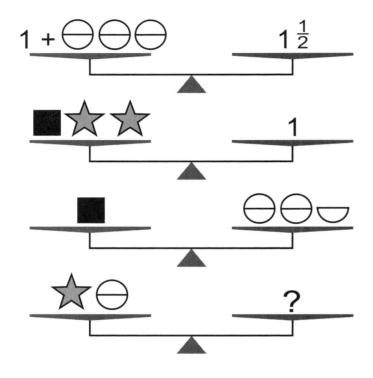

Problem 1

? = ...

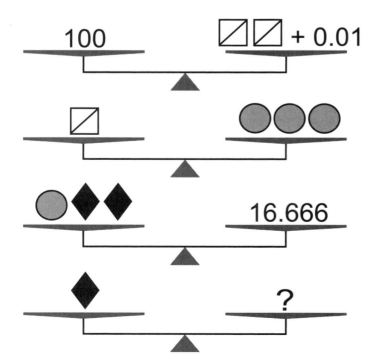

Problem 2

? = ...

Use the balanced scales to find the missing numbers.

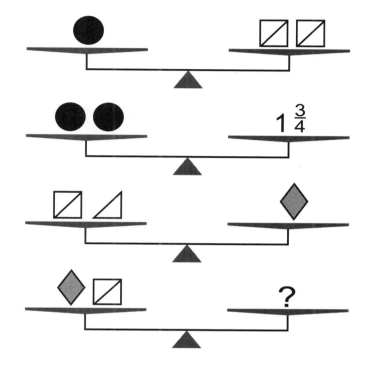

Problem 1

? = _____

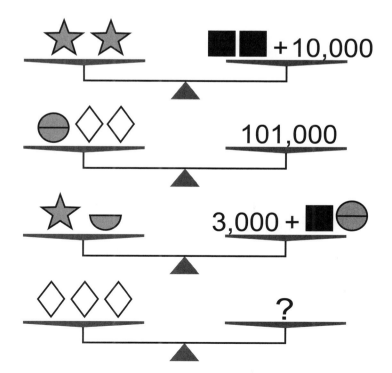

Problem 2

? = _____

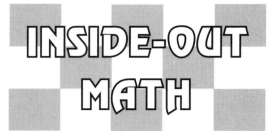

Use the clues to find the missing values.

Problem 1

a	a•c	a•d
8	96	200
b	b•c	b•d
....	....	300
c	d	
....	....	

Problem 2

a	a•c	a•d
....	3,500,000	350,000
b	b•c	b•d
500	350,000	....
c	d	
....	....	

Problem 3

a	a•c	a•d
....	225	....
b	b•c	b•d
....	375	625
c	d	
15	....	

Problem 4

a	a•c	a•d
....	....	6,500
b	b•c	b•d
....	520	20,000
c	d	
....	500	

Problem 5

a	a•c	a•d
99	7,623	9,801
b	b•c	b•d
....	5,929	....
c	d	
....	....	

Problem 6

a	a•c	a•d
....	525	735
b	b•c	b•d
101	5,050	....
c	d	
....	....	

Use the balanced scales
to find the missing numbers.

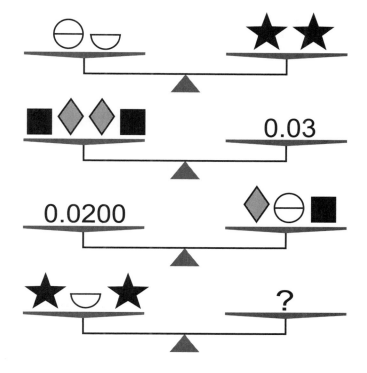

Problem 1

? = ...

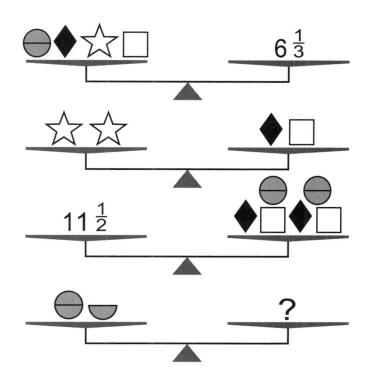

Problem 2

? = ...

All rows, columns, and four numeral diagonals must add up to the same total. Find the sum and then fill in the empty spaces.

Problem 1

30	5	50	15
		66	
47		21	
9			46

Total: ....

Problem 2

	5	179	69
139	38		
	44		
177	413		7

Total: ....

Problem 3

			52
201	259		68
311			419
383	642		460

Total: ....

Problem 4

176			464	132
		104	388	
542	191	94		
66				

Total: ....

Use the balanced scales
to find the missing numbers.

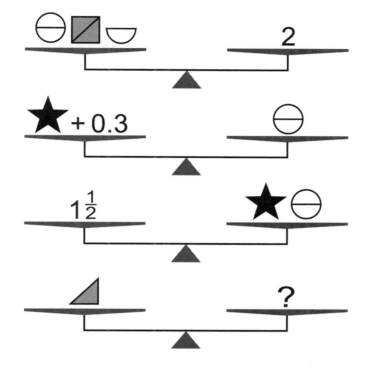

Problem 1

? = _____

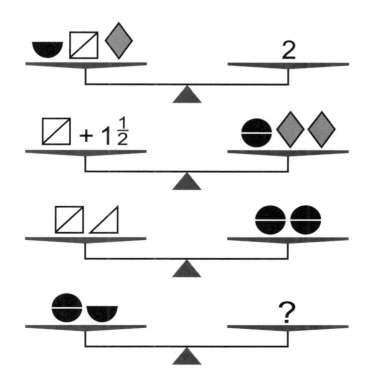

Problem 2

? = _____

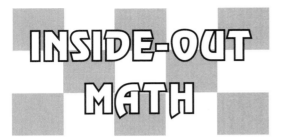

Use the clues to find the missing values.

Problem 1

a		a•c	a•d
$\frac{1}{3}$		....	$\frac{2}{3}$
b		b•c	b•d
....		$2\frac{1}{4}$	$1\frac{1}{2}$

c	d
....	....

Problem 2

a		a•c	a•d
....		30	45
b		b•c	b•d
$\frac{4}{5}$		....	48

c	d
....	....

Problem 3

a		a•c	a•d
....		21	....
b		b•c	b•d
....		14	12

c	d
$\frac{7}{8}$	....

Problem 4

a		a•c	a•d
....		6	....
b		b•c	b•d
....		$\frac{1}{8}$	$2\frac{1}{4}$

c	d
....	3

Problem 5

a		a•c	a•d
....		150	....
b		b•c	b•d
....		60	$\frac{1}{5}$

c	d
100	....

Problem 6

a		a•c	a•d
....		30	45
b		b•c	b•d
....		....	75

c	d
$\frac{5}{12}$	....

Use the balanced scales
to find the missing numbers.

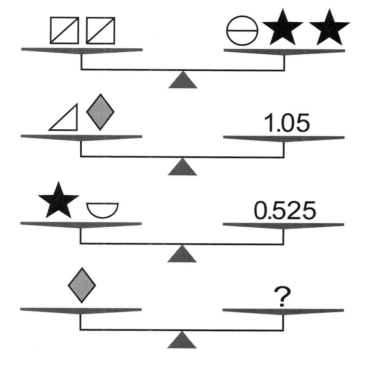

Problem 1

? = ...

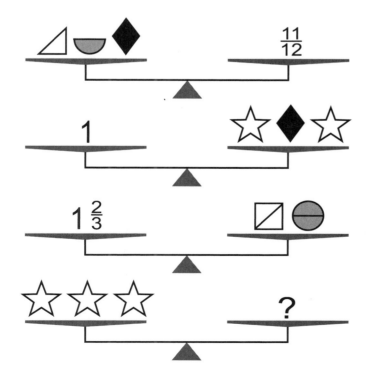

Problem 2

? = ...

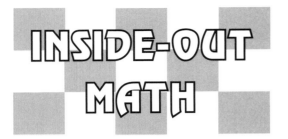
INSIDE-OUT MATH

Use the clues to find the missing values.

Problem 1

a	a•c	a•d
1.1	0.011	....
b	**b•c**	**b•d**
....	0.001	0.01

c	d
....	....

Problem 2

a	a•c	a•d
....	12	0.12
b	**b•c**	**b•d**
3.6	....	0.36

c	d
....	....

Problem 3

a	a•c	a•d
....	1.8	5
b	**b•c**	**b•d**
....	....	25

c	d
0.9	....

Problem 4

a	a•c	a•d
....	0.01	0.1
b	**b•c**	**b•d**
....	0.000001	....

c	d
....	0.001

Problem 5

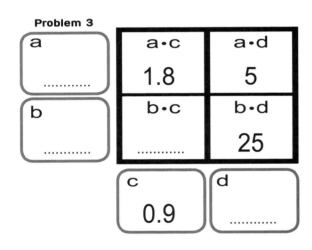

a	a•c	a•d
....		20.7
b	**b•c**	**b•d**
....	19.6	48.3

c	d
2.8	....

Problem 6

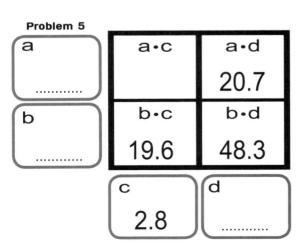

a	a•c	a•d
....	62.25	72.21
b	**b•c**	**b•d**
9.6	....	83.52

c	d
....	....

Use the balanced scales
to find the missing numbers.

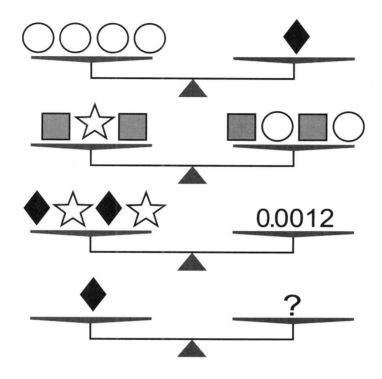

Problem 1

? = ...

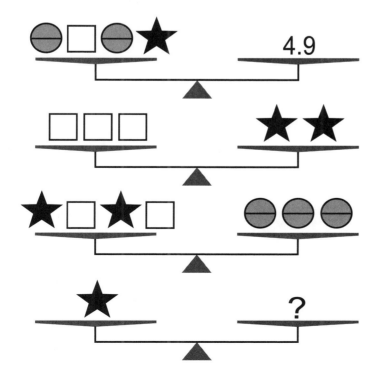

Problem 2

? = ...

Tic Tac Math

All rows, columns, and four numeral diagonals must add up to the same total. Find the sum and then fill in the empty spaces.

Problem 1

407			451
583	671	781	
979			
869	517	341	

Total: ....

Problem 2

	6		399
	468	184	255
450	180		
	346	273	

Total: ....

Problem 3

$\frac{1}{7}$	$\frac{1}{14}$	$\frac{5}{21}$	$\frac{5}{14}$
$\frac{3}{14}$	$\frac{8}{21}$		
	$\frac{1}{21}$		$\frac{1}{3}$
$\frac{2}{7}$			

Total: ....

Problem 4

	$\frac{1}{600}$	$\frac{3}{400}$	$\frac{7}{600}$
$\frac{1}{150}$	$\frac{1}{80}$	$\frac{1}{300}$	$\frac{1}{400}$
			$\frac{13}{1,200}$
	$\frac{1}{100}$		

Total: ....

INSIDE-OUT MATH

Use the clues to find the missing values.

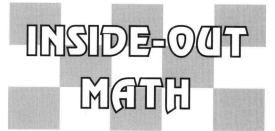

Problem 1

a		a÷c	a÷d
7,000		....	**0.7**
b		b÷c	b÷d
....		**600**	**21**

c	d
....	....

Problem 2

a		a÷c	a÷d
....		$\frac{1}{2}$	....
b		b÷c	b÷d
8		$\frac{2}{3}$	$\frac{1}{3}$

c	d
....	....

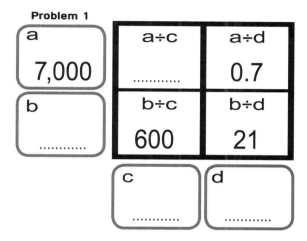

Problem 3

a		a÷c	a÷d
....		$\frac{10}{100}$	$\frac{10}{10,000}$
b		b÷c	b÷d
....		....	$\frac{100}{10,000}$

c	d
1,000	....

Problem 4

a		a÷c	a÷d
....		$1\frac{1}{3}$	$2\frac{2}{9}$
b		b÷c	b÷d
....		$2\frac{2}{3}$	....

c	d
....	**45**

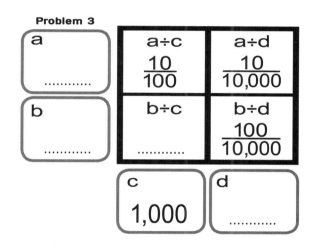

Problem 5

a		a÷c	a÷d
1,000		....	$90\frac{10}{11}$
b		b÷c	b÷d
....		$3\frac{1}{33}$	$9\frac{1}{11}$

c	d
....	....

Problem 6

a		a÷c	a÷d
....		$\frac{33}{100}$	....
b		b÷c	b÷d
....		$\frac{6}{15}$	$\frac{2}{15}$

c	d
300	....

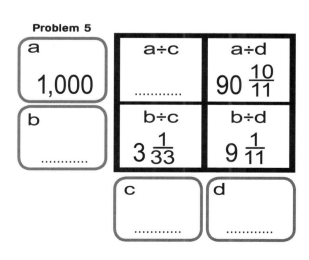

Use the balanced scales
to find the missing numbers.

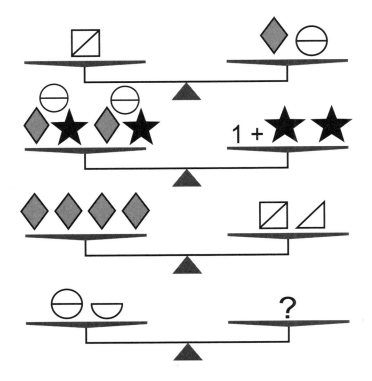

Problem 1

? = _____

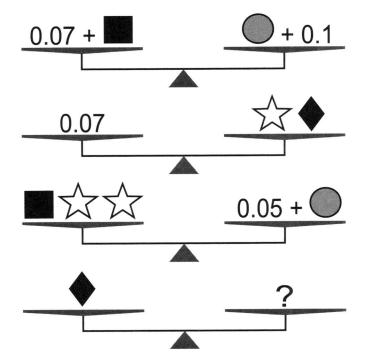

Problem 2

? = _____

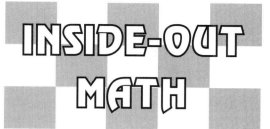
INSIDE-OUT MATH

Use the clues to find the missing values.

Problem 1

a	$\frac{3}{4}$

a÷c $1\frac{1}{2}$	a÷d $2\frac{1}{4}$
b÷c $1\frac{1}{3}$	b÷d ....

b	....

c	d ....

Problem 2

a	....

a÷c	a÷d 9
b÷c $1\frac{3}{4}$	b÷d 21

b	14

c	d ....

Problem 3

a	....

a÷c $1\frac{1}{8}$	a÷d $3\frac{3}{4}$
b÷c	b÷d $4\frac{3}{8}$

b	....

c $\frac{2}{3}$	d ....

Problem 4

a	....

a÷c $3\frac{3}{5}$	a÷d $1\frac{1}{2}$
b÷c 5	b÷d ....

b	....

c	d $\frac{2}{5}$

Problem 5

a	$\frac{1}{8}$

a÷c $\frac{1}{12}$	a÷d $\frac{1}{20}$
b÷c $\frac{1}{6}$	b÷d ....

b	....

c	d ....

Problem 6

a	....

a÷c $\frac{14}{22}$	a÷d ....
b÷c $\frac{38}{44}$	b÷d $\frac{57}{88}$

b	....

c	d $7\frac{1}{3}$

Use the balanced scales
to find the missing numbers.

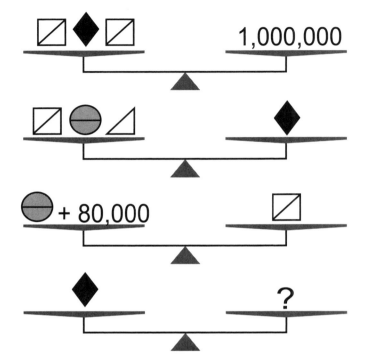

Problem 1

? = ...

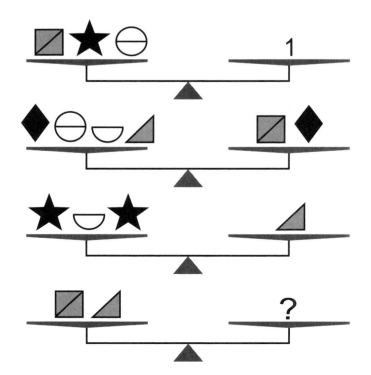

Problem 2

? = ...

Tic Tac Math

All rows, columns, and five numeral diagonals must add up to the same total. Find the sum and then fill in the empty spaces.

Problem 1

				190
191	199		195	
204	192	200	208	196
	205	188	201	
	193	206		202

Total: ....

Problem 2

0.00018	0.00031			0.0001
0.00011	0.00019			
0.00024	0.00012		0.00028	0.00016
	0.00025	0.00008	0.00021	
	0.00013	0.00026	0.00009	

Total: ....

Use the balanced scales
to find the missing numbers.

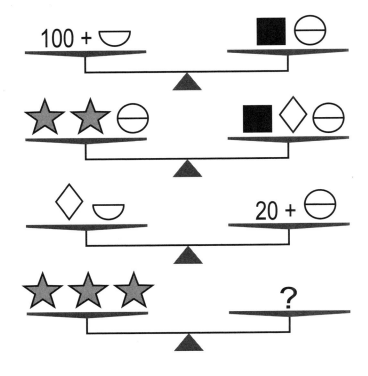

Problem 1

? = ...

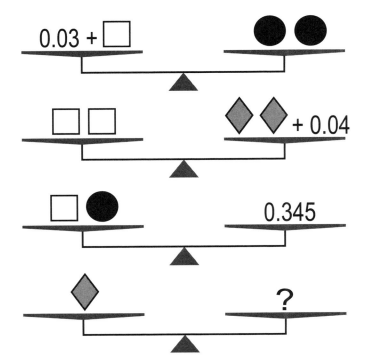

Problem 2

? = ...

Use the balanced scales
to find the missing numbers.

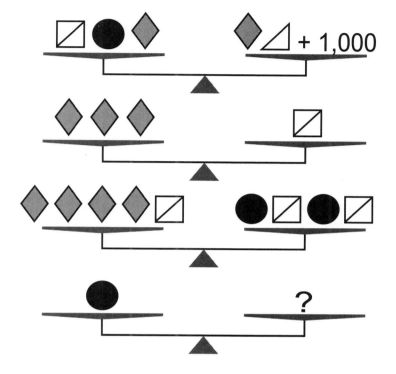

Problem 1

? = ...

Problem 2

? = ...

BALANCE MATH™ HINTS

Page 1
Problem 1: Divide both sides on 1st balance in half.
Problem 2: Substitute ●■ from 2nd balance for ◇ on 1st balance.

Page 3
Problem 1: Divide both sides on 2nd balance in thirds.
Problem 2: Divide both sides on 3rd balance in fourths.

Page 4
Problem 1: Divide both sides on 1st balance in half.
Problem 2: Divide both sides on 2nd balance in half.

Page 5
Problem 1: Divide both sides on 1st balance in half.
Problem 2: Divide both sides on 1st balance in fourths.

Page 7
Problem 1: Divide both sides on 2nd balance in thirds.
Problem 2: Remove □ from both sides on 1st balance.

Page 9
Problem 1: Substitute ■■■ from 2nd balance for ○ on 3rd balance.
Problem 2: Divide both sides on 3rd balance in fifths.

Page 10
Problem 1: Remove 500 from both sides on 1st balance.
Problem 2: Remove ⊖⧄ from both sides on 3rd balance.

Page 12
Problem 1: Remove ● from both sides on 3rd balance.
Problem 2: Remove 10,000 from both sides on 2nd balance.

Page 14
Problem 1: Substitute 0.025 from 1st balance for ★ on 2nd balance.
Problem 2: Substitute 100 + ⧄ from 3rd balance for each ◆ on 2nd balance.

Page 15
Problem 1: Divide both sides on 1st balance in half.
Problem 2: Divide both sides on 3rd balance in half.

Page 17
Problem 1: Remove ⊖ from both sides on 3rd balance.
Problem 2: Divide both sides on 3rd balance in thirds.

Page 18
Problem 1: Substitute 2,000 from 1st balance for ◆☆■ on 3rd balance.
Problem 2: Remove □ from both sides on 2nd balance.

Page 20
Problem 1: Remove 1 from both sides on 1st balance.
Problem 2: Remove 0.01 from both sides on 1st balance.

Page 21
Problem 1: Divide both sides on 2nd balance in half.
Problem 2: Divide both sides on 1st balance in half.

Page 23
Problem 1: Divide both sides on 2nd balance in half.
Problem 2: Divide both sides on 3rd balance in half.

Page 25
Problem 1: Substitute ★ + 0.3 from 2nd balance for ⊖ on 3rd balance.
Problem 2: Divide both sides on 2nd balance in half.

Page 27
Problem 1: Double both sides on 3rd balance.
Problem 2: Divide both sides of 3rd balance in half.

Page 29
Problem 1: Remove ■■ from both sides on 2nd balance.
Problem 2: Divide both sides on 3rd balance in half.

Page 32
Problem 1: Remove ★★ from both sides on 2nd balance.
Problem 2: Remove 0.07 from both sides on 1st balance.

Page 34
Problem 1: Substitute ⊖ + 80,000 and ◡ + 40,000 from 3rd balance for ⧄ and ◺, respectively, on 2nd balance.
Problem 2: Remove ◆ and ◢ from both sides on 2nd balance.

Page 36
Problem 1: Substitute 100 + ◡ from 1st balance for ■⊖ on 2nd balance.
Problem 2: Reverse 2nd balance and combine with 1st balance.

Page 37
Problem 1: Remove ◆◺ from both sides on 1st balance.
Problem 2: Add ◢ to both sides on 1st balance.

ANSWERS

Page 1

Problem 1: ? = 75

Explanation: Divide both sides on 1st balance in half, so ◇ = 500. Substitute 500 for ◇ on 2nd balance so ■ ■ + 500 = 750. Remove 500 from both sides so ■ ■ = 250. Divide both sides in half so ■ = 125. Substitute 125 for ■ on 3rd balance so ○ ○ + 125 = 275. Remove 125 from both sides so ○ ○ = 150. Divide in half so ○ = 75.

Problem 2: ? = 225

Explanation: Substitute ●■ from 2nd balance for ◇ on 1st balance so 1,000 = ●■■■. Divide both sides in half so 500 = ●■. Substitute 500 for ●■ on 3rd balance so 500 + ★ ★ = 650. Remove 500 from both sides so ★ ★ = 150. Divide both sides in half so ★ = 75. ★ ★ ★ = 75 · 3 = 225.

Page 2

Problem 1:	Problem 2:
b = 200	a = 345
c = 900	c = 296
d = 9,900	d = 358
b + d = 10,100	a + d = 703

Problem 3:	Problem 4:
a = 2,563	a = 10,845
b = 3,724	b = 12,654
d = 5,097	c = 11,369
a + c = 6,851	b + c = 24,023

Problem 5:	Problem 6:
$a = 1\frac{3}{4}$	$a = \frac{1}{4}$
$c = \frac{1}{2}$	$c = \frac{1}{3}$
$d = 1\frac{1}{3}$	$d = \frac{2}{3}$
$a + d = 3\frac{1}{12}$	$a + d = \frac{11}{12}$

Page 3

Problem 1: ? = 1,150

Explanation: Divide both sides on 2nd balance in thirds so ○ = 700. Substitute 700 for ○ on 3rd balance so ■ ■ + 700 = 1,000. Remove 700 from both sides so ■ ■ = 300. Divide both sides in half so ■ = 150. Substitute 150 for ■ and 700 for ○ on 1st balance so 150 + 700 + ◇ = 2,000. Remove 850 from both sides so ◇ = 1,150.

Page 4 (Problem 2 top right)

Problem 2: ? = 2,250

Explanation: Divide both sides on 3rd balance in fourths so ○ = 250. Substitute 250 for ○ on 1st balance so 850 = ★ ★ + 250. Remove 250 from both sides so 600 = ★ ★. Divide both sides in half so 300 = ★. Substitute 300 for each ★ on 2nd balance so 300 + 300 + 300 = 900 = ▱. Divide both sides in half so 450 = △. ▱ ▱ △ = 450 · 5 = 2,250.

Page 4

Problem 1: $? = \frac{1}{3}$

Explanation: Divide both sides on 1st balance in half so ▽ = $1\frac{1}{2}$. Substitute $1\frac{1}{2}$ for each ▽ on 2nd balance so $1\frac{1}{2} + 1\frac{1}{2} + 1\frac{1}{2} = 4\frac{1}{2} = $ ■. Substitute $4\frac{1}{2}$ for each ■ on 3rd balance so ◇ ◇ ◇ + $4\frac{1}{2}$ + $4\frac{1}{2}$ = 10. Remove 9 from both sides so ◇ ◇ ◇ = 1. Divide both sides in thirds so ◇ = $\frac{1}{3}$.

Problem 2: $? = 6\frac{3}{4}$

Explanation: Divide both sides on 2nd balance in half so □ = $3\frac{1}{2}$. Substitute $3\frac{1}{2}$ for each □ on 1st balance so $3\frac{1}{2} + 3\frac{1}{2} + 3\frac{1}{2} = 10\frac{1}{2} = $ ★. Substitute $10\frac{1}{2}$ for each ★ on 3rd balance so ○ ○ + $10\frac{1}{2}$ + $10\frac{1}{2}$ = 30. Remove 21 from both sides so ○ ○ = 9. Divide in fourths so ▽ = $2\frac{1}{4}$. ◗ ◗ = $2\frac{1}{4}$ · 3 = $6\frac{3}{4}$.

Page 5

Problem 1: ? = 1,275

Explanation: Divide both sides on 1st balance in half so ■ ☆ = 150. Substitute 150 for ■ ☆ on 2nd balance so 150 + ● = 1,050. Remove 150 from both sides so ● = 900. Substitute 900 for ● on 3rd balance so 900 + ◇ ◇ = 1,750. Remove 900 from both sides so ◇ ◇ = 850. Divide both sides in half so ◇ = 425. ◇ ◇ ◇ = 425 · 3 = 1,275.

Problem 2: ? = 3

Explanation: Divide both sides on 1st balance in fourths so △ = $3\frac{1}{4}$. Substitute $3\frac{1}{4}$ for each △ on 2nd balance so $3\frac{1}{4} + 3\frac{1}{4} + 3\frac{1}{4} = 9\frac{3}{4} = $ ○. Substitute $9\frac{3}{4}$ for ○ on 3rd balance so $9\frac{3}{4} + $ ◆ = $10\frac{1}{2}$. Remove $9\frac{3}{4}$ from both sides so ◆ = $\frac{3}{4}$. ◆ ◆ ◆ ◆ = $\frac{3}{4}$ · 4 = 3.

Page 6

Problem 1:   b = 30,000
     c = 1,111
     d = 1,010
     a - b = 8,889

Problem 2:   a = 723
     c = 478
     d = 356
     a - d = 367

Problem 3:   a = 6,042
     b = 8,105
     d = 5,698
     b - c = 5,738

Problem 4:   a = 13,007
     b = 16,040
     c = 5,279
     b - d = 4,682

Problem 5:   b = $\frac{3}{4}$
     c = $\frac{1}{4}$
     d = $\frac{1}{8}$
     a - d = $\frac{3}{8}$

Problem 6:   a = $2\frac{1}{3}$
     b = $2\frac{1}{2}$
     d = $1\frac{1}{4}$
     b - c = $\frac{5}{12}$

Page 7

Problem 1:   ? = $\frac{1}{6}$

Explanation: Divide both sides on 2nd balance in thirds so [circle] = $\frac{1}{3}$. Substitute $\frac{1}{3}$ for each [circle] on 1st balance so [square] + $\frac{1}{3}$ + $\frac{1}{3}$ = $1\frac{1}{3}$. Remove $\frac{2}{3}$ from both sides so [square] = $\frac{2}{3}$. Substitute $\frac{2}{3}$ for [square] on 3rd balance so $\frac{2}{3}$ + [diamond][diamond] = 1. Remove $\frac{2}{3}$ from both sides so [diamond][diamond] = $\frac{1}{3}$. Divide both sides in half so [diamond] = $\frac{1}{6}$.

Problem 2:   ? = 11,750

Explanation: Remove [square] from both sides on 1st balance so [star][circle][star][circle] = 7,500. Divide both sides in half so [star][circle] = 3,750. Substitute 3,750 for [star][circle] on 2nd balance so [diamond][diamond] + 3,750 = 10,750. Remove 3,750 from both sides so [diamond][diamond] = 7,000. Substitute 7,000 for [diamond][diamond] on 3rd balance so 7,000 + [square] = 15,000. Remove 7,000 from both sides so [square] = 8,000. [square][circle][star] = 8,000 + 3,750 = 11,750.

Page 8

Problem 1:

430	1,390	370
670	730	790
1,090	70	1,030

Total: 2,190

Problem 2:

184	104	120
72	136	200
152	168	88

Total: 408

Problem 3:

119	623	497
791	413	35
329	203	707

Total: 1,239

Problem 4:

8.8	27.2	19.2
28.8	18.4	8
17.6	9.6	28

Total: 55.2

Problem 5:

1.16	1.71	0.94
1.05	1.27	1.49
1.6	0.83	1.38

Total: 3.81

Problem 6:

1.669	0.199	1.249
0.619	1.039	1.459
0.829	1.879	0.409

Total: 3.117

Page 9

Problem 1:   ? = 4,500

Explanation: Substitute [square][square][square] from 2nd balance for [circle] on 3rd balance so [square][square][square][square][star] = [star] + 1,000. Remove [star] from both sides so [square][square][square][square] = 1,000. Divide both sides in fourths so [square] = 250. Substitute 250 for each [square] on 2nd balance so [circle] = 250 + 250 + 250 = 750. Substitute 750 for [circle] on 1st balance so [diamond] + 750 = 3,000. Remove 750 from both sides so [diamond] = 2,250. [diamond][diamond] = 2,250 • 2 = 4,500.

Problem 2:   ? = 675

Explanation: Divide both sides on 3rd balance in fifths so [half-circle] = 150. Remove [star] from both sides on 2nd balance so [diamond] = [circle][circle]. Substitute 150 for each [half-circle] on 2nd balance so [diamond] = 150 + 150 + 150 +150 = 600. Substitute 600 for [diamond] and 150 for each [half-circle] on 1st balance so 150 + 150 + 600 = 900 = [square]. Divide both sides in fourths so [triangle] = 225. [square][triangle] = 225 • 3 = 675.

Page 10

Problem 1:   ? = 30

Explanation: Remove 500 from both sides on 1st balance so [diamond][diamond] = 500. Divide both sides in half so [diamond] = 250. Substitute 250 for [diamond] on 2nd balance [triangle][triangle][triangle] + 250 = 3,010. Remove 250 from both sides [triangle][triangle][triangle] = 2,760. Divide both sides in sixths so [triangle] = 460. Substitute 460 for [triangle] on 3rd balance so 500 = 460 + [half-circle][half-circle]. Remove 460 from both sides so 40 = [half-circle][half-circle]. Divide both sides in fourths so 10 = [half-circle]. [half-circle][half-circle] = 10 • 3 = 30.

Problem 2:   ? = 1.5

Explanation: Remove [half-circle][square] from both sides on 3rd balance so [star][star] = 1.0. Divide both sides in half so [star] = 0.5. Divide both sides on 2nd balance in fifths so [triangle] = 0.9. Substitute 0.9 for each [triangle] and 0.5 for [star] on 1st balance so [circle] + 1.1 = 0.9 + 0.9 + 0.9 + 0.9 + 0.5 = 4.1. Remove 1.1 from both sides so [circle] = 3.0. Divide both sides in half so [half-circle] = 1.5.

Page 11

Problem 1: $b = \frac{5}{12}$
$c = \frac{3}{4}$
$d = \frac{1}{6}$
$a + d = \frac{5}{6}$

Problem 2: $a = 3\frac{4}{5}$
$c = 1\frac{3}{5}$
$d = \frac{7}{10}$
$a + c = 5\frac{2}{5}$

Problem 3: $a = \frac{5}{24}$
$b = \frac{2}{3}$
$d = \frac{11}{12}$
$b + c = 1\frac{1}{24}$

Problem 4: $a = 3\frac{1}{3}$
$b = 4\frac{1}{12}$
$c = 1\frac{3}{4}$
$a - c = 1\frac{7}{12}$

Problem 5: $b = 8\frac{1}{9}$
$c = 5\frac{1}{2}$
$d = 1\frac{1}{4}$
$b - d = 6\frac{31}{36}$

Problem 6: $b = 4\frac{4}{11}$
$c = 1\frac{7}{8}$
$d = 2\frac{9}{10}$
$a - d = \frac{1}{2}$

Page 12

Problem 1: $? = 8\frac{1}{2}$

Explanation: Remove 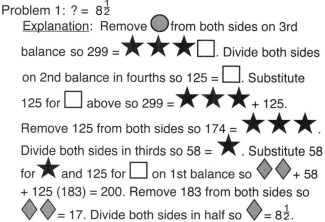 from both sides on 3rd balance so 299 = ★ ★ ★ □. Divide both sides on 2nd balance in fourths so 125 = □. Substitute 125 for □ above so 299 = ★ ★ ★ + 125. Remove 125 from both sides so 174 = ★ ★ ★. Divide both sides in thirds so 58 = ★. Substitute 58 for ★ and 125 for □ on 1st balance so ◆ ◆ + 58 + 125 (183) = 200. Remove 183 from both sides so ◆ ◆ = 17. Divide both sides in half so ◆ = 8½.

Problem 2: $? = 110{,}000$

Explanation: Remove 10,000 from both sides on 2nd balance so ■ ■ = 90,000. Divide both sides in half so ■ = 45,000. Substitute 45,000 for ■ on 1st balance so 45,000 + ◆ ◆ = 115,000. Remove 45,000 from both sides so ◆ ◆ = 70,000. Divide both sides in half so ◆ = 35,000. Substitute 35,000 for ◆ on 3rd balance so ⊖ ▽ + 35,000 = 200,000. Remove 35,000 from both sides so ⊖ ▽ = 165,000. Divide both sides in thirds so ▽ = 55,000. ⊖ = 55,000 · 2 = 110,000.

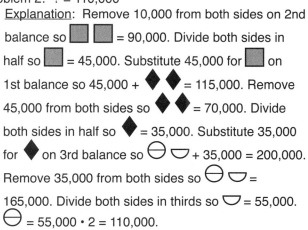

Page 13

Problem 1:

$\frac{3}{4}$	1	2
$2\frac{1}{2}$	$1\frac{1}{4}$	0
$\frac{1}{2}$	$1\frac{1}{2}$	$1\frac{3}{4}$

Total: $3\frac{3}{4}$

Problem 2:

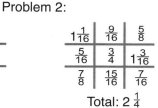

$1\frac{1}{16}$	$\frac{9}{16}$	$\frac{5}{8}$
$\frac{5}{16}$	$\frac{3}{4}$	$1\frac{3}{16}$
$\frac{7}{8}$	$\frac{15}{16}$	$\frac{7}{16}$

Total: $2\frac{1}{4}$

Problem 3:

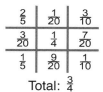

$\frac{2}{5}$	$\frac{1}{20}$	$\frac{3}{10}$
$\frac{3}{20}$	$\frac{1}{4}$	$\frac{7}{20}$
$\frac{1}{5}$	$\frac{9}{20}$	$\frac{7}{10}$

Total: $\frac{3}{4}$

Problem 4:

$\frac{9}{48}$	$\frac{1}{48}$	$\frac{1}{6}$
$\frac{5}{48}$	$\frac{1}{8}$	$\frac{7}{48}$
$\frac{1}{12}$	$\frac{11}{48}$	$\frac{1}{16}$

Total: $\frac{3}{8}$

Problem 5:

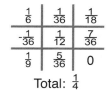

$\frac{1}{6}$	$\frac{1}{36}$	$\frac{1}{18}$
$-\frac{1}{36}$	$\frac{1}{12}$	$\frac{7}{36}$
$\frac{1}{9}$	$\frac{5}{36}$	0

Total: $\frac{1}{4}$

Problem 6:

$\frac{1}{400}$	$\frac{1}{200}$	$-\frac{3}{400}$
$-\frac{1}{100}$	0	$\frac{1}{100}$
$\frac{3}{400}$	$-\frac{1}{200}$	$-\frac{1}{400}$

Total: 0

Page 14

Problem 1: $? = 0.1$

Explanation: Substitute 0.025 from 1st balance for ★ on 2nd balance so 0.05 = ● □ + 0.025. Remove 0.025 from both sides so 0.025 = ● □. Substitute 0.025 for each ● □ on 3rd balance so 0.025 + 0.025 + ◆ ◆ = 0.25. Remove 0.05 from both sides so ◆ ◆ = 0.20. Divide both sides in half so ◆ = 0.1.

Problem 2: $? = 19{,}100$

Explanation: Substitute 100 + ◣ from 3rd balance for each ◆ on 2nd balance so 100 + 100 + ◣ ◣ ◣ = 2,900. Remove 200 from both sides so ◣ ◣ ◣ = 2,700. Divide both sides in sixths so ◣ = 450. Substitute 450 for ◣ on 1st balance so ▽ + 450 = 10,000. Remove 450 from both sides so ▽ = 9,550. ⊖ = 9,550 · 2 = 19,100.

Page 15

Problem 1: ? = $1\frac{1}{5}$

Explanation: Divide both pans on 1st balance in half so ⬤ = $\frac{9}{10}$. Substitute $\frac{9}{10}$ for ⬤ on 3rd balance so $\frac{1}{10} + \frac{9}{10} = $ ◇◇◇◇◇. Divide both sides in fifths so $\frac{1}{5}$ = ◇. Substitute $\frac{1}{5}$ for ◇ on 2nd balance so 1 = ◤ + $\frac{1}{5}$. Remove $\frac{1}{5}$ from both sides so ◤ = $\frac{4}{5}$. Divide in half so ◢ = $\frac{4}{10}$ and ◢◢ = $\frac{4}{10}$ · 3 = $1\frac{1}{5}$.

Problem 2: ? = 465,000

Explanation: Divide both sides on 3rd balance in half so 190,000 = ◆. Substitute 190,000 for ◆ on 1st balance so ▱▱▱△ = 190,000 + 300,000 = 490,000. Divide both sides in sevenths so △ = 70,000. Substitute 70,000 for △ on 2nd balance so 70,000 + ⬤ = 1,000,000. ⬤ = 930,000 and ⬤ = 465,000.

Page 16

Problem 1: b = 0.01
c = 0.1
d = 1.11
b + d = 1.12

Problem 2: a = 3.7
c = 9.3
d = 2.4
a + c = 13

Problem 3: a = 0.005
b = 0.5
d = 0.005
b + d = 0.505

Problem 4: a = 3.03
b = 3.3
c = 0.33
b - d = 0.297

Problem 5: b = 0.66
c = 0.06
d = 0.006
b - c = 0.6

Problem 6: a = 1.001
b = 1.01
c = 0.1
a - d = 1.0009

Page 17

Problem 1: ? = 70

Explanation: Remove ⊖ from both sides on 3rd balance so 350 = ◆◆. Divide both sides in half so 175 = ◆. Substitute 175 for ◆ on 1st balance so 300 = ▪ + 175. Remove 175 from both sides so 125 = ▪. Remove ◆ from both sides on 2nd balance so ▪ + 50 = ⊖⊖▽. Substitute 125 for ▪ so 125 + 50 = 175 = ⊖⊖▽. Divide both sides in fifths so ▽ = 35. ⊖ = 35 · 2 = 70.

Page 18 — Problem 2: ? = $1\frac{7}{8}$

Explanation: Divide both sides on 3rd balance in thirds so △ = $4\frac{1}{2}$. Double both sides so ▱ = 9. Substitute 9 for ▱ on 2nd balance so 2 + 9 = 11 = ◆⬤☆. Substitute $10\frac{3}{8}$ from 1st balance for ⬤☆ above, so 11 = ◆ + $10\frac{3}{8}$. Remove $10\frac{3}{8}$ from both sides so $\frac{5}{8}$ = ◆ and ◆◆◆ = $\frac{5}{8}$ · 3 = $1\frac{7}{8}$.

Page 18

Problem 1: ? = 200

Explanation: Substitute 2,000 from 1st balance for ◆☆▪ on 3rd balance so 500 + ⊖⊖▽ = 2,000. Remove 500 from both sides so ⊖⊖▽ = 1,500. Divide both sides in fifths so ▽ = 300. Double so ⊖ = 600. Substitute 600 for each ⊖ on 2nd balance so ▪◆ = 600 + 600 + 600 = 1,800. Substitute 1,800 for ◆▪ on 1st balance so 2,000 = 1,800 + ☆. Remove 1,800 from both sides so ☆ = 200.

Problem 2: ? = $5\frac{7}{8}$

Explanation: Remove ▢ from both sides on 2nd balance so ◆◆ = $2\frac{1}{3}$. Divide both sides in half so ◆ = $1\frac{1}{6}$. Substitute $1\frac{1}{6}$ for ◆ on 3rd balance so ⬤ = $3\frac{7}{12}$ + $1\frac{1}{6}$ = $4\frac{3}{4}$. Substitute $4\frac{3}{4}$ for each ⬤ on 1st balance so $3\frac{5}{8}$ + ▢ = $4\frac{3}{4}$ + $4\frac{3}{4}$ = $9\frac{1}{2}$. Remove $3\frac{5}{8}$ from both sides so ▢ = $5\frac{7}{8}$.

Page 19

Problem 1: b = $1\frac{1}{2}$
c = $\frac{5}{6}$
d = $1\frac{7}{24}$
a + d = $2\frac{1}{24}$

Problem 2: a = $\frac{5}{6}$
c = $\frac{1}{5}$
d = $\frac{3}{8}$
a - c = $\frac{19}{30}$

Problem 3: a = $2\frac{1}{12}$
b = $1\frac{1}{3}$
d = $\frac{7}{8}$
b - c = $\frac{17}{24}$

Problem 4: a = 0.07
b = 0.7
c = 0.07
b - d = 0.693

Problem 5: b = 0.101
c = 1.01
d = 0.011
b + c = 1.111

Problem 6: a = 0.009
b = 0.0909
d = 0.0009
a - d = 0.0081

Page 20

Problem 1: ? = $\frac{11}{24}$

Explanation: Remove 1 from both sides on 1st balance so ⊖ ⊖ ⊖ = $\frac{1}{2}$. Divide both sides in sixths so ▽ = $\frac{1}{12}$. Substitute $\frac{1}{12}$ for each ▽ on 3rd balance so ■ = $\frac{1}{12} + \frac{1}{12} + \frac{1}{12} + \frac{1}{12} + \frac{1}{12} = \frac{5}{12}$. Substitute $\frac{5}{12}$ for ■ on 2nd balance so $\frac{5}{12}$ + ★ ★ = 1. Remove $\frac{5}{12}$ from both sides so ★ ★ = $\frac{7}{12}$ and ★ = $\frac{7}{24}$. ★ ⊖ = $\frac{7}{24} + \frac{1}{6} = \frac{11}{24}$.

Problem 2: ? = 0.0005

Explanation: Remove 0.01 from both sides on 1st balance so 99.99 = ▱ ▱. Divide both sides in half so 49.995 = ▱. Substitute 49.995 for ▱ on 2nd balance so 49.995 = ◯ ◯ ◯. Divide both sides in thirds so ◯ = 16.665. Substitute 16.665 for on 3rd balance so 16.665 + ◆ ◆ = 16.666. Subtract 16.665 from both sides so ◆ ◆ = 0.001. Divide in half so ◆ = 0.0005.

Page 21

Problem 1: ? = $1\frac{3}{32}$

Explanation: Divide both sides on 2nd balance in half so ● = $\frac{7}{8}$. Substitute $\frac{7}{8}$ for ● on 1st balance so $\frac{7}{8}$ = ▱ ▱. Divide both sides in fourths so $\frac{7}{32}$ = △. Substitute $\frac{7}{32}$ for each △ on 3rd balance so $\frac{7}{32} + \frac{7}{32} + \frac{7}{32} = \frac{21}{32}$ = ◆. So ◆ ▱ = $\frac{21}{32} + \frac{7}{16} = 1\frac{3}{32}$.

Problem 2: ? = 145,500

Explanation: Divide both sides on 1st balance in half so ★ = ■ + 5,000. Substitute ■ + 5,000 for ★ on 3rd balance so ◗ ■ + 5,000 = 3,000 + ■ ◯. Remove 3,000 and ■ from both sides so 2,000 = ◗. Substitute 2,000 for ◗ on 2nd balance so 2,000 + 2,000 + ◇ ◇ = 101,000. Remove 4,000 from both sides so ◇ ◇ = 97,000. ◇ = 48,500 and ◇ ◇ ◇ = 48,500 · 3 = 145,500.

Page 22

Problem 1: b = 12
c = 12
d = 25
b · c = 144

Problem 2: a = 5,000
c = 700
d = 70
b · d = 35,000

Problem 3: a = 15
b = 25
d = 25
a · d = 375

Problem 4: a = 13
b = 40
c = 13
a · c = 169

Problem 5: b = 77
c = 77
d = 99
b · d = 7,623

Problem 6: a = $10\frac{1}{2}$
c = 50
d = 70
b · d = 7,070

Page 23

Problem 1: ? = 0.01

Explanation: Divide both sides on 2nd balance in half so ■ ◆ = 0.015. Substitute 0.015 for ■ ◆ on 3rd balance so 0.0200 = ◯ + 0.015. Remove 0.015 from both sides so 0.005 = ◯ and 0.0025 = ▽. Thus ◯ ⌣ = 0.0075. Substitute 0.0075 for ◯ ▽ on first balance so 0.0075 = ★ ★. ★ ⌣ ★ = 0.0075 + 0.0025 = 0.01.

Problem 2: ? = $6\frac{7}{8}$

Explanation: Divide both sides on 3rd balance in half so $5\frac{3}{4}$ = ◑ ◆ ▱. Substitute $5\frac{3}{4}$ for ▱ on 1st balance so $5\frac{3}{4}$ + ☆ = $6\frac{1}{3}$. So ☆ = $\frac{7}{12}$. Substitute $\frac{7}{12}$ for each ☆ on 2nd balance so $\frac{7}{12} + \frac{7}{12}$ = $1\frac{1}{6}$ = ◆ ▱. Substitute $1\frac{1}{6}$ for ◆ ▱ above so $5\frac{3}{4}$ = ◑ + $1\frac{1}{6}$. Remove $1\frac{1}{6}$ from both sides so ◑ = $4\frac{7}{12}$. ◑ ⌣ = $4\frac{7}{12} + 2\frac{7}{24} = 6\frac{7}{8}$.

Page 24

Problem 1:

30	5	50	15
14	3	66	17
47	10	21	22
9	82	-37	46

Total: 100

Problem 2:

247	5	179	69
139	38	210	113
-63	44	208	311
177	413	-97	7

Total: 500

Problem 3:

104	5	838	52
201	259	471	68
311	93	176	419
383	642	-486	460

Total: 999

Problem 4:

176	5	464	132
-7	104	388	292
542	191	94	-50
66	477	-169	403

Total: 777

Page 25

Problem 1: ? = 0.325

Explanation: Substitute ★ + 0.3 from 2nd balance so $1\frac{1}{2}$ = 1.5 = ★ ★ + 0.3. Remove 0.3 from both sides so 1.2 = ★ ★ and 0.6 = ★ . Substitute 0.6 for ★ on 2nd balance so 0.6 + 0.3 = 0.9 = ◯ and ▽ = 0.45. Substitute 0.9 for ◯ and 0.45 for ▽ on 1st balance so 0.9 + 0.45 (1.35) + ▨ = 2. Remove 1.35 from both sides so ▨ = 0.65. Divide both sides in half so ◢ = 0.325.

Problem 2: ? = $\frac{15}{16}$

Explanation: Divide both sides on 2nd balance in half so △ + $\frac{3}{4}$ = ⬤ ◆ . Substitute △ + $\frac{3}{4}$ for ⬤ ◆ on 1st balance so ◻ △ + $\frac{3}{4}$ = 2. Remove $\frac{3}{4}$ from both side so ◻ △ = $1\frac{1}{4}$. Substitute $1\frac{1}{4}$ for ◻ △ on 3rd balance so $1\frac{1}{4}$ = ⬤ ⬤ . Divide both sides in fourths so $\frac{5}{16}$ = ⬤ . ⬤ ⬤ = $\frac{5}{16}$ • 3 = $\frac{15}{16}$.

Page 26

Problem 1: b = $\frac{3}{4}$
c = 3
d = 2
a • c = 1

Problem 2: a = $\frac{3}{4}$
c = 40
d = 60
b • c = 32

Problem 3: a = 24
b = 16
d = $\frac{3}{4}$
a • d = 18

Problem 4: a = 36
b = $\frac{3}{4}$
c = $\frac{1}{6}$
a • d = 108

Problem 5: a = $1\frac{1}{2}$
b = $\frac{3}{5}$
d = $\frac{1}{3}$
a • d = $\frac{1}{2}$

Problem 6: a = 72
b = 120
d = $\frac{5}{8}$
b • c = 50

Page 27

Problem 1: ? = 0.7875

Explanation: Double both sides on 3rd balance so ★ ★ ◯ = 1.05. Substitute 1.05 for ★ ★ ◯ on 1st balance so ◻ ◻ = 1.05. Divide in fourths so △ = 0.2625. Substitute 0.2625 for △ on 2nd balance so 0.2625 + ◆ = 1.05. Subtract 0.2625 from both sides so ◆ = 0.7875.

Problem 2: ? = $1\frac{3}{8}$

Explanation: Divide both sides of 3rd balance in half so $\frac{5}{6}$ = △ ⬤ . Substitute $\frac{5}{6}$ for △ ⬤ on 1st balance so $\frac{5}{6}$ + ◆ = $\frac{11}{12}$. Thus ◆ = $\frac{1}{12}$. Substitute $\frac{1}{12}$ for ◆ on 2nd balance so 1 = ☆ ☆ + $\frac{1}{12}$. Remove $\frac{1}{12}$ form both sides so $\frac{11}{12}$ = ☆ ☆ . Divide in half so $\frac{11}{24}$ = ☆ . ☆ ☆ ☆ = $\frac{11}{24}$ • 3 = $1\frac{3}{8}$.

Page 28

Problem 1: b = 0.1
c = 0.01
d = 0.1
a • d = 0.11

Problem 2: a = 1.2
c = 10
d = 0.1
b • c = 36

Problem 3: a = 2
b = 10
d = 2.5
b • c = 9

Problem 4: a = 100
b = 0.01
c = 0.0001
b • d = 0.00001

Problem 5: a = 3
b = 7
d = 6.9
a • c = 8.4

Problem 6: a = 8.3
c = 7.5
d = 8.7
b • c = 72

Page 29

Problem 1: ? = 0.0004

Explanation: Remove ▨ ▨ from both sides on 2nd balance so ☆ = ◯ ◯ . Substitute ☆ for each ◯ ◯ on 1st balance so ☆ ☆ = ◆ . Substitute ◆ for ☆ ☆ on 3rd balance so ◆ ◆ ◆ = 0.0012. Divide in thirds so ◆ = 0.0004.

Problem 2: ? = 1.26

Explanation: Divide both sides on 3rd balance in half so ★ ◻ = ⬤ ⬤ . Substitute ⬤ ⬤ for ★ ◻ on 1st balance so ⬤ ⬤ ⬤ ⬤ = 4.9. Divide both sides in sevenths so ⬤ = 0.7 and ⬤ ⬤ = 0.7 x 6 = 4.2. Substitute 4.2 for ⬤ ⬤ on 3rd balance so ★ ◻ ★ ◻ = 4.2. Substitute ◻ ◻ ◻ from 2nd balance for ★ ★ above so ◻ ◻ ◻ ◻ ◻ = 4.2. Divide both in fifths so ◻ = 0.84. Thus ◻ ◻ ◻ = 0.84 + 0.84 + 0.84 = 2.52. Substitute 2.52 for ◻ ◻ ◻ on 2nd balance so 2.52 = ★ ★ . Divide in half so ★ = 1.26.

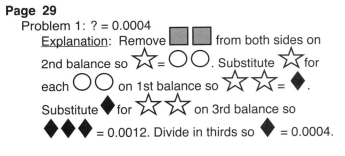

Page 30

Problem 1:

407	913	1,067	451
583	671	781	803
979	737	649	473
869	517	341	1,111

Total: 2,838

Problem 2:

220	6	375	399
93	468	184	255
450	180	168	202
237	346	273	144

Total: 1,000

Problem 3:

$\frac{1}{7}$	$\frac{1}{14}$	$\frac{5}{21}$	$\frac{5}{14}$
$\frac{3}{14}$	$\frac{8}{21}$	$\frac{5}{42}$	$\frac{2}{21}$
$\frac{1}{6}$	$\frac{1}{21}$	$\frac{11}{42}$	$\frac{1}{3}$
$\frac{2}{7}$	$\frac{13}{42}$	$\frac{4}{21}$	$\frac{1}{42}$

Total: $\frac{17}{21}$

Problem 4:

$\frac{1}{240}$	$\frac{1}{600}$	$\frac{3}{400}$	$\frac{7}{600}$
$\frac{1}{150}$	$\frac{1}{80}$	$\frac{1}{300}$	$\frac{1}{400}$
$\frac{1}{200}$	$\frac{1}{1,200}$	$\frac{1}{120}$	$\frac{13}{1,200}$
$\frac{11}{1,200}$	$\frac{1}{100}$	$\frac{7}{1,200}$	0

Total: $\frac{1}{40}$

Page 31

Problem 1: b = 210,000
c = 350
d = 10,000
a ÷ c = 20

Problem 2: a = 6
c = 12
d = 24
a ÷ d = $\frac{1}{4}$

Problem 3: a = 100
b = 1,000
d = 100,000
b ÷ c = 1

Problem 4: a = 100
b = 200
c = 75
b ÷ d = 4$\frac{4}{9}$

Problem 5: b = 100
c = 33
d = 11
a ÷ c = 30$\frac{10}{33}$

Problem 6: a = 99
b = 120
d = 900
a ÷ d = $\frac{11}{100}$

Page 32

Problem 1: ? = $\frac{15}{32}$

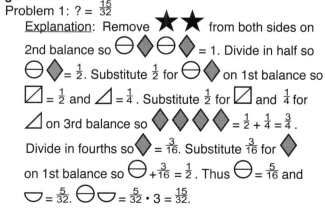

Explanation: Remove ★ ★ from both sides on 2nd balance so ⊖ ◆ ⊖ ◆ = 1. Divide in half so ⊖ ◆ = $\frac{1}{2}$. Substitute $\frac{1}{2}$ for ⊖ ◆ on 1st balance so ▱ = $\frac{1}{2}$ and △ = $\frac{1}{4}$. Substitute $\frac{1}{2}$ for ▱ and $\frac{1}{4}$ for △ on 3rd balance so ◆ ◆ ◆ = $\frac{1}{2}$ + $\frac{1}{4}$ = $\frac{3}{4}$. Divide in fourths so ◆ = $\frac{3}{16}$. Substitute $\frac{3}{16}$ for ◆ on 1st balance so ⊖ + $\frac{3}{16}$ = $\frac{1}{2}$. Thus ⊖ = $\frac{5}{16}$ and ▽ = $\frac{5}{32}$. ⊖ ▽ = $\frac{5}{32}$ · 3 = $\frac{15}{32}$.

Problem 2: ? = 0.06

Explanation: Remove 0.07 from both sides on 1st balance so ■ = ◯ + 0.03. Substitute ◯ + 0.03 for ■ on 3rd balance so 0.03 + ◯ + ☆ ☆ = 0.05 + ◯. Remove 0.03 and ◯ from both sides so ☆ ☆ = 0.02 and ☆ = 0.01. Substitute 0.01 for ☆ on 2nd balance so 0.07 = 0.01 + ◆. Remove 0.01 from both sides so ◆ = 0.06.

Page 33

Problem 1: b = $\frac{2}{3}$
c = $\frac{1}{2}$
d = $\frac{1}{3}$
b ÷ d = 2

Problem 2: a = 6
c = 8
d = $\frac{2}{3}$
a ÷ c = $\frac{3}{4}$

Problem 3: a = $\frac{3}{4}$
b = $\frac{7}{8}$
d = $\frac{1}{5}$
b ÷ c = 1$\frac{5}{16}$

Problem 4: a = $\frac{3}{5}$
b = $\frac{5}{6}$
c = $\frac{1}{6}$
b ÷ d = 2$\frac{1}{12}$

Problem 5: b = $\frac{1}{4}$
c = 1$\frac{1}{2}$
d = 2$\frac{1}{2}$
b ÷ d = $\frac{1}{10}$

Problem 6: a = 3$\frac{1}{2}$
b = 4$\frac{3}{4}$
c = 5$\frac{1}{2}$
a ÷ d = $\frac{21}{44}$

Page 34

Problem 1: ? = 520,000

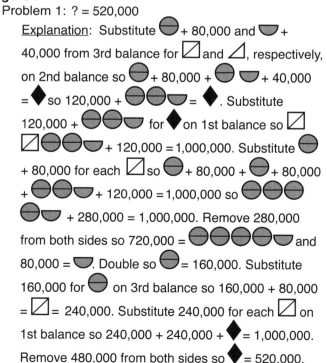

Explanation: Substitute ◯ + 80,000 and ◡ + 40,000 from 3rd balance for ◿ and △, respectively, on 2nd balance so ◯ + 80,000 + ◯ ◡ + 40,000 = ◆ so 120,000 + ◯ ◯ ◡ = ◆. Substitute 120,000 + ◯ ◯ ◡ for ◆ on 1st balance so ◿ ◿ ◯ ◯ ◡ + 120,000 = 1,000,000. Substitute ◯ + 80,000 for each ◿ so ◯ + 80,000 + ◯ + 80,000 + ◯ ◯ ◡ + 120,000 = 1,000,000 so ◯ ◯ ◯ ◯ ◡ + 280,000 = 1,000,000. Remove 280,000 from both sides so 720,000 = ◯ ◯ ◯ ◯ ◡ and 80,000 = ◡. Double so ◯ = 160,000. Substitute 160,000 for ◯ on 3rd balance so 160,000 + 80,000 = ◿ = 240,000. Substitute 240,000 for each ◿ on 1st balance so 240,000 + 240,000 + ◆ = 1,000,000. Remove 480,000 from both sides so ◆ = 520,000.

Problem 2: ? = 1

Explanation: Remove 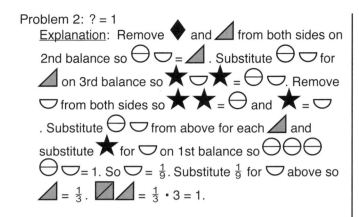 and ▲ from both sides on 2nd balance so ◒ ▽ = ▲. Substitute ◒ ▽ for ▲ on 3rd balance so ★ ▽ ★ = ◒ ▽. Remove ▽ from both sides so ★ ★ = ◒ and ★ = ▽. Substitute ◒ ▽ from above for each ▲ and substitute ★ for ▽ on 1st balance so ◯◯◯ ◒ ▽ = 1. So ▽ = $\frac{1}{9}$. Substitute $\frac{1}{9}$ for ▽ above so ▲ = $\frac{1}{3}$. ▰▲ = $\frac{1}{3}$ · 3 = 1.

Page 35

Problem 1:

198	211	194	207	190
191	199	212	195	203
204	192	200	208	196
197	205	188	201	209
210	193	206	189	202

Total: 1,000

Problem 2:

0.00018	0.00031	0.00014	0.00027	0.0001
0.00011	0.00019	0.00032	0.00015	0.00023
0.00024	0.00012	0.0002	0.00028	0.00016
0.00017	0.00025	0.00008	0.00021	0.00029
0.0003	0.00013	0.00026	0.00009	0.00022

Total: 0.001

Page 36

Problem 1: ? = 180

Explanation: Substitute 100 + ▽ from 1st balance for ▰◒ on 2nd balance so ★ ★ ◒ = ◇ + 100 + ▽. Remove ▽ from both sides on 3rd balance so ◇ = 20 + ▽. Substitute 20 + ▽ for ◇ above so ★ ★ ◒ = ▽ ▽ + 20 + 100. Remove ◒ from both sides so ★ ★ = 120 and ★ = 60. ★ ★ ★ = 60 · 3 = 180.

Problem 2: ? = 0.20

Explanation: Reverse 2nd balance and combine with 1st balance so 0.07 + ☐ ◆ ◆ = ☐ ● ☐ ●. Double both sides on 3rd balance so ☐ ● ☐ ● = 0.69. Substitute 0.69 for ☐ ● ☐ ● above so 0.07 + ☐ ◆ ◆ = 0.69. Divide both sides on 2nd balance in half so ☐ = ◆ + 0.02. Substitute ◆ + 0.02 for ☐ above so 0.07 + 0.02 + ◆ ◆ ◆ = 0.69. Remove 0.09 from both sides so ◆ ◆ ◆ = 0.60. ◆ = 0.20.

Page 37

Problem 1: ? = 250

Explanation: Remove ◆ ◿ from both sides on 1st balance so ● ◿ = 1,000. Remove ☐ from both sides on 3rd balance so ◆ ◆ ◆ ◆ = ● ☐ ●. Divide both sides in half so ◆ ◆ = ● ◿. Substitute ◆ ◆ for ● ◿ above so ◆ ◆ = 1,000 and so ◆ ◆ ◆ = 1,500. Substitute 1,500 for ◆ ◆ ◆ on 2nd balance so 1,500 = ☐. Substitute 1,500 for ☐ above and 500 for each ◆ above so 500 + 500 + 500 + 500 = ● + 1,500 + ●. Remove 1,500 from both sides so ● ● = 500 and ● = 250.

Problem 2: ? = 1$\frac{1}{4}$

Explanation: Add ◿ to both sides on 1st balance so ◆ ⊕ ◿ = 2 + ◿ ◿. Substitute 1 + ◆ ◆ from 2nd balance for ⊕ ◿ above so ◆ ◆ ◆ + 1 = 2 + ◿ ◿. Divide both sides on 3rd balance in thirds so ◿ = $\frac{1}{6}$ and ◿ ◿ = $\frac{1}{4}$. Substitute $\frac{1}{4}$ for ◿ ◿ above so ◆ ◆ ◆ + 1 = 2 + $\frac{1}{4}$ and ◆ = $\frac{5}{12}$. From above substitute $\frac{1}{6}$ for ◿ and $\frac{5}{12}$ for each ◆ on 2nd balance so $\frac{1}{6}$ + ⊕ = 1 + $\frac{5}{12}$ + $\frac{5}{12}$. ⊕ = 1$\frac{2}{3}$ and ⊕ = 1$\frac{1}{4}$.